Magic Mates

in
Hollywood

Jane West

Illustrated by
Stik

RISING★STARS

Rising Stars UK Ltd.
22 Grafton Street, London W1S 4EX
www.risingstars-uk.com

The right of Jane West to be identified as the author of this work
has been asserted by her in accordance with the Copyright, Design
and Patents Act 1988.

Published 2008

Cover design: Button plc
Illustrator: Stik, Bill Greenhead for Illustration
Text design and typesetting: Andy Wilson
Publisher: Gill Budgell
Editor: Jane Wood

British Library Cataloguing in Publication Data.
A CIP record for this book is available from the British Library

ISBN: 984 1 84680 334 5

Printed in the UK by CPI Bookmarque, Croydon, CR0 4TD

Mixed Sources
Product group from well-managed
forests and other controlled sources
www.fsc.org Cert no. TT-COC-002227
© 1996 Forest Stewardship Council

Contents

Meet the Magic Mates

**The Magic Mates are best friends –
but that doesn't mean they're all alike.**

Name: *Izzie*

The sporty one: can climb trees, surf and take on the boys at their own game – and win.

Travels by: running!

Loves: trendy tracksuits, open skies and sandy beaches.

Hates: standing still.

Name: *Meena*

The girly one: uses her mobile for networking and planning her social life.

Travels by: Mum's car (her personal chauffeur).

Loves: pink and her Magic Mates.

Hates: breaking a nail.

Name: *Ginger*

The ginger one: you don't wanna mess with this feisty gal – the Kung Fu and quick quip queen!

Travels by: push-scooter.

Loves: Jackie Chan and her Magic Mate pals.

Hates: nail extensions.

Name: Jo

The clever one: uses her brains and quick wit to talk her way out of trouble. Sometimes she's a bit too quick.

Travels by: bicycle and is designing a pair of motorised rollerblades.

Loves: Jacqueline Wilson, Cathy Cassidy and Albert Einstein.

Hates: being called 'geek', 'nerd', 'swot' or 'boffin'.

Name: Ellie

The fashion-conscious one: can tell her Prada from her Asda and knows how to accessorise.

Travels by: limousine, of course! (But only in her dreams.)

Loves: shopping.

Hates: anything to do with getting dirty; anyone who upsets her Magic Mates.

Name: Yash

The funky punky one: the 'alternative' one of the gang who hugs trees, people and furry animals.

Travels by: skateboard.

Loves: having a good time.

Hates: bullies.

First Class
All the Way

Ellie has won first place in a magazine
competition. The prize is a trip
to Hollywood to meet the stars.
Of course, her Magic Mates
are going too!

Ginger   Wow! I've never travelled in a car like this before! It's even got a fridge in it!

Ellie   Yeah, it's great, isn't it?

Meena   I wish I could travel in cars like this all the time.

Yash   It wouldn't fit on your drive!

Ginger   It wouldn't fit in my street!

Izzie   It's not very green.

Meena   No, it's bright pink.
I love it!

Jo   I wonder what this button does?

Driver Yes, ma'am?
            How may I help you?

Jo   Oh, er, hi!
            I was just wondering
            where we are.

Driver You're in Hollywood, ma'am.
            And here's your hotel.

The Magic Mates look up at a huge hotel.
It has palm trees at the front. Some very
rich-looking people are going inside.

Meena Oh look! There's Paris Wilson –
and her little dog has the same
outfit!

Jo Poor dog.

Yash   Look! There's Alex McCool.
             He's so …

Izzie   Cool?

Driver   So what are you girls
             going to do in Hollywood?

Ginger   Climb the Hollywood sign!

Jo   Visit a film studio.

Yash and Izzie

     Go surfing at Malibu beach!

Meena   Go shopping!

Ellie   See the stars!

Driver   Here's a map of where the stars live.

Ellie   Wow! Thanks! That's great!

All the Magic Mates want to see a film being made. Luckily, Ellie's prize includes a guided tour around the GMG film studios. Hollywood heartthrob Brad Tipp is making a new film there. All the Magic Mates hope they can meet him.

Meena Brad Tipp … oh …
he's so good-looking.

Izzie He really cares about
the environment, too.

Ginger I heard he does all his own stunts
in his films.

Yash And he's a really good surfer.

Jo He writes his own scripts
sometimes. He must be
really clever.

Ellie Look! There he is!

Jo Quick! Let's follow him.
We can get him to sign
his name for us.

The girls run after Brad. Which way
did he go? Did he go into the film studio,
or towards the canteen, or into
the private area where only
the actors can go?

Meena   Oh no. I think we've lost him.

Ginger   We've got a better chance
              of finding him if we split up.

Ellie   Yes. Let's meet back here
              in ten minutes.
              Come on, Jo!

A Touch of Hollywood Magic

Ellie and Jo head towards the private area where only the actors are allowed.

Jo   Let's knock on this door.
        They might be able to help us.

Ellie   Excuse me. I'm sorry to bother
you, but did Brad Tipp come this
way? We were hoping to get him
to sign his name for us.

Honey   Sorry, girls. He didn't come in
here. Oh, hey, aren't you Ellie –
the girl who won the guided tour
prize?

Ellie   Yes, that's me!

Honey   We've been expecting you.
The boss told us to show you
how films are made.
Come on in.

The girls follow Honey into a huge
film studio. It's nearly as big
as a football pitch.

Honey   This is a film set.
It's the background we use
when we shoot a film.
You might recognise it …

Ellie   It looks like the set for
the new *Antman* film!
I recognise those buildings.

Jo   It looks so real in the film.
But really it's just made of wood
and cardboard and paint.
It's really clever, but isn't it
sort of cheating?

Honey   Do you think Antman is real?

Jo   No, of course not!

Ellie   I wish he was real.

Honey   Then it's not really cheating, is it? Because you know it's not real, but you enjoy it anyway. Making films is like making a little bit of magic. And don't forget, it takes a lot of hard work to make a film.

Ellie   I thought it was fun to make films.

Honey   Yes, it's lots of fun, but hard work, too. Lots of people work very hard to make each film. Some people make wonderful sets like this one, someone writes the story (it's called the script), and there are the people who make the costumes ...

Ellie   And the actors …

Honey   Yes, and the director,
the producer, the makeup
people, the camera crew …
Oh! It takes hundreds of people
to make a film!

5

A Light Moment

Honey takes the girls to meet
the people who do the lighting.

Honey   This is Lenny.
           He does the lighting on films.

Ellie   I thought you just used daylight.

Lenny Sometimes, but not in a studio like this. I can use these big lights to make it look like a bright summer day, or a dark, winter day. And look, I can use this light to make it look like the moon is shining.

Jo   That's amazing. I didn't know there was so much work to do the lighting for a film.

Lenny   And don't forget there are the sound people who record the actors' voices. They're very important, as well.

26

Ellie	Lenny, do you know lots of famous actors?
Lenny	Yes, Bette David, Elizabeth Trailer, Richard Burdons – all the great ones.
Ellie	I don't know any of them.
Honey	Perhaps you'll know some of the actors that I have met: Julia Robbins, Keanu Rooves, Toby McQuire and Kristy Dunns.

Ellie   Do you know Brad Tipp?

Honey   Yes.

Ellie   He's my favourite actor.
He's so handsome and clever.
And he's got lovely hair –
it's so thick and shiny.

Jo   What's he like?

Honey   Er … Er … A bit different
            from how he looks in films.
            Now, let's go and meet some
            of the stunt artists. Some of them
            really do jump off high buildings
            and crash cars – thanks to
            the magic of Hollywood!

Ellie   I wonder why she didn't
            want to talk about Brad Tipp?

Jo   Yes, it's a bit odd, isn't it?
            I wonder what's going on …

Brad Tipp's Secret

Honey takes the girls into
the costume department.

Ellie   Look at all these
            beautiful clothes!

Jo   There's a suit of armour
            over there, just like a real knight!

Ellie   And these dresses are just like
              the ones I've seen in books –
              ladies wore them hundreds
              of years ago.

Honey   These costumes are for a new
              film starring Brad Tipp.
              He plays a knight who has to
              save a princess. He's had to learn
              to use a sword. It's not as easy
              as it looks in films.

Jo notices a small door, with a poster of
Brad Tipp.

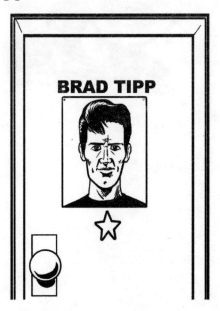

Jo What's in here?

Honey No! Don't go in there!

But it's too late. Jo has opened the door and looked inside.

Jo   Oh no! It's awful!
              Don't go in there, Ellie!
              You don't want to see him
              like that!

Ellie   See who? What? Aaaaaagh!
              That hamster has escaped!

Jo   That's not a hamster, it's …

Honey   Er … that's Mr Tipp's wig.

Brad Tipp Hello, girls. Oh dear,
I seem to have dropped my wig.
Don't worry – it won't bite.
Do you want me to sign
my name for you?

Jo Er, yeah, thanks.

Ellie But … but … What happened
to your hair?

Brad Tipp Oh, well, this is my real hair.
Or not! I always wear a wig
when I'm making a film.

Poor Ellie. She's so disappointed
to see that Brad Tipp's hair isn't real.
He doesn't have any hair at all.
He's bald. Really bald.

Ellie   But his hair looks so real in films!

Honey   I'm sorry you had to see that,
Ellie.

Jo   So that's the magic
of Hollywood?

Honey   Sometimes I think that it spoils the dream when people find out how films are made. Isn't it better to enjoy the magic?

Ellie   Yes. I like the magic better.

Jo   Don't be too disappointed, Ellie. And don't forget, Brad Tipp is still a good actor.

Honey   Yes, that's a special kind of
magic, too ... even if he is as bald
as a potato. Now, shall we go
and see the makeup department?

Ellie   No, thanks. I think I've seen
enough magic for today.

Jo   I can think of one kind of magic
you'd like to see.

Ellie   Like what?

The Magic Mates!

Jo   Well, don't forget that your
         Mates are Magic, too!

About the Author

Jane West's favourite film scene is in *Toy Story*, when Buzz Lightyear realises that he's not really an astronaut, but a toy. It makes her laugh and cry at the same time.

Jane West:

- lives by the beach in Cornwall
- likes taking her dog Pip paddling in the sea
- loves bodyboarding
- has worked in an art gallery, a bookshop and a school.

Now she's a writer, and has had great fun writing about the Magic Mates. She hopes you liked reading about them.

Hollywoodland

Did you know that Hollywood used to be called 'Hollywoodland'? The famous Hollywood sign was put up in 1923. Each letter was 17 metres high and 10 metres wide. A bad storm blew away the last four letters and so the area became just Hollywood!

Famous film quotes

'Our comedies are not to be laughed at.'
Film boss Samuel Goldwyn

'The secret to film is that it's an illusion.'
George Lucas, maker of the *Star Wars* films

Hollywood History

- The first film was made in Hollywood in 1910. It was a silent film (there was no sound, just the pictures), and it was called *In Old California*.

- The first Hollywood film star was Mary Pickford. She was an actress from Canada.

- The first Hollywood TV station opened in 1947.

- The Hollywood Walk of Fame began in 1958. Famous actors and actresses had their 'star' on the pavement. They signed their name and made an imprint of their hands in wet concrete.

Fun Facts

★ *Children in Hollywood go to school at ... Hollywood High.*

★ The cartoon family The Simpsons have a star on the Hollywood Walk of Fame.

★ *By the time you're 65, you'll have watched nine years of television!*

★ 25% of all DVDs sold are cartoons.

★ *The first movie to use sound was*
The Jazz Singer *in 1927. The first words,*
spoken by Al Jolson, were: 'Wait a minute,
you ain't heard nothing yet.'

★ An 'extra' is someone in a film who doesn't
have any speaking parts. In 1982 the film
Ghandi had 300,000 extras!

★ Spider-Man 3 *cost over $250,000,000*
to make!

Hollywood Lingo

How to talk like a filmstar!

Hollyweird – A spooky film.

Random – Not good, as in, 'Her clothes are so random!'

Awesome – Great, fantastic.

Blow out of here – Leave, as in, 'Let's blow out of here now.'

A bust – Failure or disappointment, as in, 'That party was a bust.'

Catch some rays – Sunbathe, as in, 'I think I'll catch some rays.'

Couch potato – Lazy person.

Get with it – Hurry up.

Go bananas – Go crazy, as in,
'I'll go bananas if I can't have some chocolate.'

Goofed up – Made a mistake.

Party-hearty – Celebrate, as in, 'I did well
in that test so I'm going to party-hearty.'

Rinky-dink – Not very good, as in,
'I didn't like that book, it was totally rinky-dink.'

Vibes – Feelings, as in, 'I've got a good vibe
about that new teacher.'

Hollywood Quiz

1 What was the first film ever made in Hollywood?

2 Where do kids go to school in Hollywood?

3 Is it a good thing if someone says your outfit is random?

4 What's a film 'extra'?

5 How many years of TV will you have watched by the time you're 32 and a half?

How did you score?

0–1 Oh dear! You'd be a bust in Hollywood!

2–3 Not bad, more party-hearty than rinky-dink!

4–5 Awesome!

Magic Mates

RISING ★ STARS

Magic Mates books are available from most booksellers.

For mail order information
please call Rising Stars on 0871 47 23 010
or visit www.risingstars-uk.com